Garfield

Wraps it up

BY: JIM DAVIS

RAVETTE BOOKS

This edition first published by
Ravette Books Limited 1987

Reprinted 1987, 1988, 1989

Printed in Great Britain
for Ravette Books Limited,
3 Glenside Estate, Star Road, Partridge Green,
Horsham, West Sussex RH13 8RA
by The Guernsey Press Company Limited,
Guernsey, Channel Islands
and bound by
WBC Bookbinders Limited,
Maesteg, Mid Glamorgan.

ISBN 0 948456 56 6

Wraps it up

You'll be surprised when you open up this new title and discover Garfield's special gift for comedy. Under the cover of his dry wit and sarcasm there lurks an inner Garfield; who's warm and lovable, buried beneath his laziness and insatiable appetite, and under that there's even more. As you can see, it takes a lot of wrapping to cover all of Garfield.

I WONDER WHAT GRANDIOSE DREAM GARFIELD IS HAVING RIGHT NOW

2-27

JIM DAVIS

© 1981 United Feature Syndicate, Inc.

HAVE YOU EVER SEEN SUCH A SAD MOVIE IN ALL YOUR LIFE, GARFIELD?

MAYBE I'M TOO HARDENED. MAYBE I'M TOO CYNICAL...

JIM DAVIS

BUT I WASN'T THAT MOVED BY "FLIPPER GETS THE ICK"

2-28

© 1981 United Feature Syndicate, Inc.

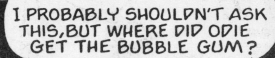

© 1985 United Feature Syndicate, Inc.

11-20 JIM DAVIS

11-21 JIM DAVIS

© 1985 United Feature Syndicate, Inc.

GOOD MORNING, MORNING

4.12

WHAT A GREAT DAY TO BE ALIVE

I'D EVEN GO SO FAR AS TO SAY IT'S A GREAT DAY TO BE AWAKE

© 1985 United Feature Syndicate Inc

JIM DAVIS

HEY, GARFIELD. HEY, ODIE. I HAVE A LITTLE PIECE OF LEFTOVER STEAK. WHO

JIM DAVIS 4-13

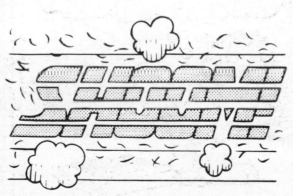

© 1985 United Feature Syndicate Inc

WANTS IT?

GARFIELD

DO YOU BOYS WANNA GO OUT?

WELL, DO YOU, HUH?

HUH? HUH? DO YUH? HUH? HUH?

OPEN THE DARN DOOR

THE DIRECT APPROACH IS THE BEST APPROACH

1-19

GARFIELD'S
Believe it, or DON'T!

CATS AND DOGS EVOLVED FROM A SINGLE ANIMAL CALLED A "COG"...IT BECAME EXTINCT WHEN IT BARKED UP THE WRONG TREE...

BARK! BARK! BARK!

A TREE NAMED "BUBBA"

Believe it, or DON'T!

JIM DAVIS 1-23

GARFIELD'S
Believe it, or DON'T!

IN 1957, A CAT IN OREGON SAVED A DROWNING CHILD

1-24

BUT, IT WAS UNDER THE LEGAL SIZE LIMIT, SO HE THREW THE KID BACK

Believe it, or DON'T!

JIM DAVIS

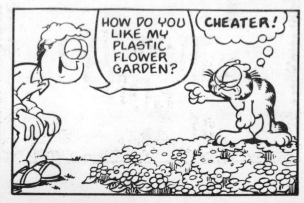

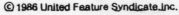

DO YOU KNOW WHAT I LOVE ABOUT CATS THE MOST? IT'S OUR DIGNITY. EVEN ROYALTY COULD LEARN FROM THE DIGNIFIED STYLE WITH WHICH WE CONDUCT OUR LIVES

JIM DAVIS 2-12

WELL, I SEE BY THE OLD CLOCK ON THE FLOOR, IT'S LUNCH TIME

© 1986 United Feature Syndicate, Inc.

TIME TO GO BEG FOR TABLE SCRAPS

2-13

JIM DAVIS

MY CAT ISN'T PERFECT. HE LIES AROUND A LOT

IN FACT, I ENCOURAGE HIM TO LIE AROUND A LOT

© 1986 United Feature Syndicate, Inc.

BECAUSE EVERY TIME HE MOVES, HE DESTROYS SOMETHING

WHIFF!

JIM DAVIS

3-5

ALLOW ME

HOW COULD YOU?! YOU STUPID BALL! I'LL SHOW YOU!

JIM DAVIS

3-6

WHIRRR!

I THINK YOU SWING TOO HARD

SCRAM! THIS IS MY BIRDBATH!

I HATE TO SEE BIRDS HAVE A GOOD TIME

HEY! THIS WATER IS FREEZING!

UNNNGH!

GARFIELD

OH-NO!

ODIE! THANK GOODNESS IT'S YOU! THROW ME A VINE!

© 1986 United Feature Syndicate, Inc.

GREAT!

NOW PULL!

5-11

PLAYING IN YOUR FOOD AGAIN, I SEE

PLAYING HECK! YOU OUGHTA PUT WARNING SIGNS AROUND THIS OATMEAL!

JIM DAVIS

A selection of Garfield books published by Ravette

Garfield Landscapes

Garfield The All-Round Sports Star	£2.95
Garfield The Irresistible	£2.95
Garfield On Vacation	£2.95
Garfield Weighs In	£2.95
Garfield I Hate Monday	£2.95
Garfield Special Delivery	£2.95
Garfield Another Serve	£2.95
Garfield The Incurable Romantic	£2.95
Garfield This Is Your Life	£2.95
Garfield Sheer Genius	£2.95
Garfield Goes Wild	£2.95

Garfield Pocket-books

No. 1	Garfield The Great Lover	£1.95
No. 2	Garfield Why Do You Hate Mondays?	£1.95
No. 3	Garfield Does Pooky Need You?	£1.95
No. 4	Garfield Admit It, Odie's OK!	£1.95
No. 5	Garfield Two's Company	£1.95
No. 6	Garfield What's Cooking?	£1.95
No. 7	Garfield Who's Talking?	£1.95
No. 8	Garfield Strikes Again	£1.95
No. 9	Garfield Here's Looking At You	£1.95
No. 10	Garfield We Love You Too	£1.95
No. 11	Garfield Here We Go Again	£1.95
No. 12	Garfield Life and Lasagne	£1.95
No. 13	Garfield In The Pink	£1.95
No. 14	Garfield Just Good Friends	£1.95
No. 15	Garfield Plays It Again	£1.95
No. 16	Garfield Flying High	£1.95
No. 17	Garfield On Top Of The World	£1.95
No. 18	Garfield Happy Landings	£1.95

Garfield TV Specials

Here Comes Garfield	£2.95
Garfield On The Town	£2.95
Garfield In The Rough	£2.95
Garfield In Disguise	£2.95
Garfield In Paradise	£2.95
Garfield Goes To Hollywood	£2.95
A Garfield Christmas	£2.95
The Second Garfield Treasury	£5.95
The Third Garfield Treasury	£5.95
The Fourth Garfield Treasury	£5.95
Garfield A Weekend Away	£4.95
Garfield How to Party	£3.95

All these books are available at your local bookshop or newsagent, or can be ordered direct from the publisher. Just tick the titles you require and fill in the form below. Prices and availability subject to change without notice.

Ravette Books Limited, 3 Glenside Estate, Star Road, Partridge Green, Horsham, West Sussex RH13 8RA

Please send a cheque or postal order, and allow the following for postage and packing. UK: Pocket-books – 45p for up to two books and 15p for each additional book. Landscape Series and TV Specials – 45p for one book plus 15p for each additional book. Treasuries, How to Party and A Weekend Away – 75p for each book.

Name...

Address...

....